Charles M. Schulz

SNOOPY
and
THE PEANUTS GANG

HIT THE HEADLINES

RAVETTE BOOKS

This edition first published by Ravette Books Limited 1989.

Printed and bound for Ravette Books Limited,
3 Glenside Estate, Star Road,
Partridge Green, Horsham,
Sussex RH13 8RA
by Mateu Cromo Artes Gráfica, s.a.

ISBN: 1 85304 109 2

PEANUTS

featuring

"Good ol' Charlie Brown"

by SCHULZ

9-16

BONK!

BONK

BONK

BONK

I DON'T KNOW WHAT'S WRONG WITH MY PASS RECEIVER... HE KEEPS COMPLAINING ABOUT HEADACHES...

PEANUTS featuring **"Good ol' Charlie Brown"** by Schulz

The last car drove away. It began to rain.

And so our hero's life ended as it had begun... a disaster.

"I never got any breaks," he had always complained.

He had wanted to be rich. He died poor. He wanted friends. He died friendless.

He wanted to be loved. He died unloved. He wanted laughter. He found only tears.

He wanted applause. He received boos. He wanted fame. He found only obscurity. He wanted answers. He found only questions.

I'M HAVING A HARD TIME ENDING THIS..

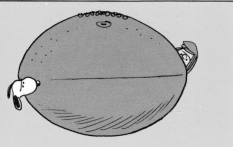

PEANUTS

featuring

"Good ol' Charlie Brown"

by Schulz

NOPE!

I'D LIKE TO HAVE YOU ON MY TEAM, CHUCK, BUT I JUST DON'T THINK YOU'RE GOOD ENOUGH...

IN FACT, I DON'T SEE ANYONE AROUND HERE WHO COULD COME UP TO MY STANDARD!

HOW ABOUT MY LINEBACKER OVER THERE? HE'S PRETTY GOOD

HIM?

OKAY, LET'S TRY HIM OUT..

HERE I COME, FELLA! STOP ME IF YOU CAN!!

FREIGHT TRAIN!!

CRUNCH! BONE-BREAKING RIB-SHAKING EAR-SPLITTING FLESH-TEARING EARTH SHATTERING TEETH RATTLING SMASH!

SOUND OF GLASS BREAKING

GOOD SHOT, KID! HOW WOULD YOU LIKE TO PLAY FOR A DECENT TEAM?

SIGH

KEEP TALKING, SWEETIE..

10-21

PEANUTS
featuring
"Good ol' Charlie Brown"
by Schulz

DO YOU LIKE JOKES AND RIDDLES?

I GUESS SO... WHY?

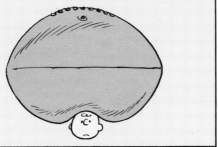

I HAVE A RIDDLE FOR YOU, CHARLIE BROWN...WHAT ARE THE THREE THINGS IN LIFE THAT ARE CERTAIN?

DEATH AND TAXES!!

THAT'S ONLY TWO...

YOU'RE RIGHT...HMM... I KNOW WHAT THE THIRD ONE IS, BUT I JUST CAN'T SEEM TO THINK... DON'T TELL ME...

RATS! I SEEM TO HAVE A MENTAL BLOCK OR SOMETHING...

IT'S SO AGGRAVATING WHEN YOU'RE TRYING TO THINK OF SOMETHING, AND YOU...

NOW, I REMEMBER!

WHAM!

IT WAS SO OBVIOUS, CHARLIE BROWN!

PEANUTS
featuring
"Good ol' CharlieBrown"
by Schulz

THEY WORK FOR DAYS AHEAD OF TIME, SEE...

AND ON THANKSGIVING DAY THEY ROAST THIS BIRD, SEE, AND THEY...

11-18

KLUNK!

OH, LITTLE FRIEND OF FRIENDS, DON'T WORRY... NO ONE IS GOING TO ROAST YOU!

IF ANYONE TRIED TO ROAST YOU FOR THANKSGIVING, YOU KNOW WHAT I'D DO?

BONK!

I'D PUNCH HIM IN THE NOSE!!

NOW, WHAT BROUGHT THAT ON?

PEANUTS
featuring
"Good ol' Charlie Brown"
by Schulz

WHAT ARE YOU WATCHING?

"CITIZEN KANE"

I'VE SEEN IT ABOUT TEN TIMES

THIS IS THE FIRST TIME I'VE EVER SEEN IT...

12-9

"ROSEBUD" WAS HIS SLED!

AAUGH!!

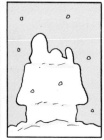

IF HE TRIES TO INSTALL A CABLE CAR AND A SUMMIT RESTAURANT, I'M LEAVING!

PEANUTS

featuring

"Good ol'
Charlie Brown"

by Schulz

PEANUTS

featuring

"Good ol' Charlie Brown"

by Schulz

Winter had come again all too soon, and it was time for Joe Jacket to bring in his polar cows.

As he rode out from the barn, the first flakes of snow began to fall.

He looked up at the slate-gray sky and shivered.

12-30

The blizzard started quickly. A howling wind pounded the snow across the bleak prairie.

Joe Jacket hunched forward in the saddle, and urged his mount forward through the flying snow and screaming wind.

TELL MY PUBLISHERS NOT TO EXPECT A MANUSCRIPT UNTIL SPRING!

Schulz

PEANUTS featuring "Good ol' CharlieBrown" by Schulz

※ SIGH ※

MY LIFE HAS NO MEANING..

EVERYTHING SEEMS EMPTY...

EVEN MY BUNNY BOOKS SEEM MEANINGLESS

I SEARCH THE SKIES, BUT I CAN FIND NO MEANING!

1-13

NO MEANING!

※ SIGH ※

AH! MEANING!!

PEANUTS

featuring

"Good ol' Charlie Brown"

by Schulz

Madam Fullcharge

I'M READY!

SO IT'S "SHOW AND TELL" TIME AGAIN, IS IT? WELL, DO I EVER HAVE A SURPRISE FOR YOU TODAY!

I HAVE A LITTLE FILM TO SHOW YOU THAT'S GONNA KNOCK YOUR EYES OUT!

NO, MA'AM... THAT'S ONLY AN EXPRESSION..

ALL RIGHT, IF I CAN HAVE A COUPLE OF YOU STRONG TYPES LIFT THIS PROJECTOR INTO PLACE, WE CAN GET THIS SHOW ON THE ROAD!

NO, LET'S PUT IT ON THAT TABLE BACK THERE... HOW ABOUT YOU FOUR WEIRDOS MOVING THAT TABLE?

AND I'LL NEED A COUPLE MORE TO PUT THIS SCREEN UP... LET'S GO!! ON THE DOUBLE, THERE!

1-20

STRETCH THAT CORD ACROSS THE BACK, AND PLUG IT INTO THAT SOCKET IN THE CORNER...

OKAY, SOMEONE RUN DOWN TO THE CUSTODIAN THEN, AND GET AN EXTENSION! YOU THERE, GET GOING!!

NOW, WHAT ABOUT THOSE WINDOW SHADES? LET'S HAVE ALL OF YOU WHO SIT ALONG THE SIDE THERE PULL DOWN THOSE STUPID SHADES..

AND I'LL NEED SOMEONE ON THE LIGHT SWITCH... ONE VOLUNTEER... YOU THERE, HONEY, GET THE SWITCH!

IS THAT THE BELL ALREADY?

OKAY, WE'LL TAKE IT TOMORROW FROM HERE.. EVERYONE BE IN PLACE BY NINE! THANK YOU, AND GOOD MORNING!

Schulz

PEANUTS
featuring
"Good ol' Charlie Brown"
by Schulz

IS THAT ALL YOU EVER DO, WATCH REPEATS?

BUZZ OFF!

✻ SIGH ✻

STOP THAT STUPID SIGHING!

THERE'S NOTHING WRONG WITH SIGHING

THERE IS IF IT BUGS SOMEONE!

IT'S SCRIPTURAL!

IT'S WHAT?!

"LIKEWISE THE SPIRIT HELPS US IN OUR WEAKNESS; FOR WE DO NOT KNOW HOW TO PRAY AS WE OUGHT, BUT THE SPIRIT HIMSELF INTERCEDES FOR US WITH SIGHS TOO DEEP FOR WORDS."

"ROMANS."...EIGHTH CHAPTER!

2-17

I DON'T KNOW...I'M EITHER GOING TO HAVE TO SLUG HIM, OR START GOING BACK TO SUNDAY SCHOOL!

PEANUTS
featuring
"Good ol' Charlie Brown"
by Schulz

SOMETIMES I THINK YOU DON'T REALIZE THAT YOU COULD LOSE ME...

2-24

ARE YOU SURE YOU WANT TO SUFFER THE TORTURES OF THE MEMORY OF A LOST LOVE?

DO YOU KNOW THE TORTURES OF THE MEMORY OF A LOST LOVE?

IT'S AWFUL!!!

IT WILL HAUNT YOU NIGHT AND DAY!!

YOU'LL WAKE UP AT NIGHT SCREAMING!

YOU CAN'T EAT! YOU CAN'T SLEEP!! YOU'LL WANT TO SMASH THINGS!

YOU'LL HATE YOURSELF AND THE WORLD AND EVERYBODY IN IT!

OOOOOOO!!!

ARE YOU SURE YOU WANT TO RISK LOSING ME?

PEANUTS
featuring
"Good ol' Charlie Brown"
by Schulz

NEXT
SHOW
1:00 P.M.

3-17

YOU KNOW
WHAT?

WHAT?

SIX HOURS IS
A LONG TIME TO
STAND HERE..

THAT'S
TRUE

BUT WHERE
ELSE ARE YOU GOING
TO SEE "WAR AND PEACE"
PERFORMED WITH
HAND PUPPETS?

PEANUTS
featuring
"Good ol' Charlie Brown"
by Schulz

PLAY ME, TRADE ME, FORGET ME.. WHO CARES?

OH, NO!

GUESS WHAT, MARCIE, I'VE DECIDED TO GIVE YOU A TRY AT CENTERFIELD THIS YEAR!

I DON'T PLAY BASEBALL, SIR...

I THINK YOU'LL BE A REAL NATURAL!

I HATE GAMES, SIR!

WHY DON'T YOU JUST TROT OUT THERE ON YOUR LITTLE BILLIE JEAN KING LEGS, AND WE'LL SEE WHAT YOU CAN DO...

I CAN'T DO ANYTHING, SIR, BECAUSE I HATE BASEBALL!

JUST REMEMBER, MARCIE, THAT WINNING IS EVERYTHING, AND LOSING IS NOTHING!

I DON'T AGREE, SIR... WINNING JUST DOESN'T MEAN THAT MUCH TO ME...

OKAY, THERE'S A NICE HIGH ONE... GET UNDER IT FAST, AND THEN WING IT ON HOME!

I HAVE NO INTEREST IN GETTING UNDER IT FAST AND WINGING IT ON HOME...

I DON'T PLAY BASEBALL, SIR!!

3-31

THE JOB'S YOURS, MARCIE! CONGRATULATIONS!!

BY THE WAY, JUST BECAUSE I'M THE MANAGER, DOESN'T MEAN YOU HAVE TO CALL ME "SIR"

YES, SIR... ✱SIGH✱

PEANUTS featuring "Good ol' Charlie Brown" by Schulz

MOM

"THERE'S NO REASON FOR YOU TO KEEP COMING BACK TO THE NEST ON MOTHER'S DAY...THAT'S NOT THE WAY WE BIRDS DO THINGS!"

5-12

"ONCE YOU'VE LEFT, LITTLE BIRD, THAT'S IT! YOU CAN'T GO HOME AGAIN! SO FLY AWAY! DON'T LOOK BACK! THE WORLD IS YOURS!"

SIGH

I MUST ADMIT SHE'S A PRETTY SHARP MOTHER!

PEANUTS
featuring
"Good ol' Charlie Brown"
by Schulz

...WHO IS CRABBIEST OF US ALL?

I HAVE A QUESTION..

I'M WATCHING TV!

DO YOU THINK I'M CRABBY?

OF COURSE! YOU'RE PROBABLY THE MOST CRABBY PERSON THE WORLD HAS EVER KNOWN!

SOME PEOPLE ARE UP ONE DAY AND DOWN THE NEXT...YOU NEVER KNOW HOW TO TAKE THEM...YOU WOULDN'T WANT ME TO BE LIKE THAT, WOULD YOU?

AND WHO CAN BE PLEASANT ALL THE TIME? NO ONE CAN BE PLEASANT ALL THE TIME... WHAT DO YOU EXPECT OF ME?

I DON'T EXPECT ANYTHING OF YOU

YOU'RE NO HELP AT ALL!

5-19

ALL RIGHT, HOW ABOUT THIS? HOW ABOUT A YEAR'S SCHEDULE WHICH GIVES YOU TWO HUNDRED PLEASANT DAYS, ONE HUNDRED "REALLY UP" DAYS, SIXTY CRABBY DAYS AND FIVE "REALLY DOWN" DAYS? I COULD LIVE WITH THAT, I THINK...

CAN WE CALL TODAY ONE OF THE "REALLY DOWN" DAYS?

SURE.. WHY NOT?

POW!!

THIS IS GOING TO BE GREAT..I STILL HAVE FOUR "REALLY DOWN" DAYS LEFT, AND I HAVEN'T EVEN TOUCHED MY SIXTY CRABBY DAYS...

PEANUTS

featuring

"Good ol' Charlie Brown"

by Schulz

PAWPET THEATER

NOW PLAYING

BEAU GESTE

INTERMISSION

THAT WAS A LONG FIRST ACT...DO YOU WANT TO WALK AROUND A BIT...MAYBE STRETCH OUR LEGS?

I COULD USE A DRINK OF WATER

HE PUTS ON A GOOD SHOW, DOESN'T HE? I'M VERY IMPRESSED...

6-30

THERE'S ONLY ONE THING HIS THEATER NEEDS...

A DRINKING FOUNTAIN!

PEANUTS

featuring

"Good ol' Charlie Brown"

by SCHULZ

I THINK I'M AWAKE

SUDDENLY, I FEEL LIKE A TOASTED ENGLISH MUFFIN WITH GRAPE JELLY....

WAM! WAM! WAM!

I KNOW THAT KICK... THAT'S THE KICK OF SOMEONE WHO'S DECIDED AT TWO O'CLOCK IN THE MORNING THAT HE NEEDS A TOASTED ENGLISH MUFFIN WITH GRAPE JELLY...

WELL, FORGET IT!!

I'M GOING TO HAVE TO LEARN TO DISGUISE THAT KICK

7-14

PEANUTS®
featuring
"Good ol' Charlie Brown"
by SCHULZ

!

SALLY! YOUR BEACH BALL IS FLOATING AWAY!

IT'S GOING CLEAR ACROSS THE LAKE!

STAY CALM, BIG BROTHER...STAY CALM!

OKAY, YOU STUPID BEACH BALL, COME BACK HERE RIGHT NOW, OR I'LL SEE TO IT THAT YOU REGRET IT FOR THE REST OF YOUR LIFE!

7-21

YOU HAVE TO KNOW HOW TO TALK TO A BEACH BALL!

PEANUTS featuring "Good ol' Charlie Brown" by Schulz

HMM.

Z

GUESS WHAT..

IF YOU'RE INTERESTED, I JUST READ ABOUT A NEW DIET...

7-28

YOU CAN EAT ALL YOU WANT..

..BUT YOU CAN'T SWALLOW! HA HA HA HA HA!

BONK!

IT'S NO FUN BEING A WAITER IF YOU CAN'T JOKE WITH THE CUSTOMERS!

SCHULZ

PEANUTS
featuring
"Good ol' Charlie Brown"
by SCHULZ

SNOOPY

OUT!!

SMASH!

KILL!!

DRIVE!

SLAM! SMACK!

8-4

OUT!!

SMASH!

KILL! KILL! KILL!!

SMASH!

NICE GAME!

PEANUTS

featuring

"Good ol' Charlie Brown"

by Schulz

PAWPET SHOW TODAY

NOW PLAYING
"IN THE BEGINNING"

Act III

HAVE YOU EVER SEEN THE ENTIRE OLD TESTAMENT PERFORMED BY PUPPETS BEFORE?

NO, I CAN'T SAY THAT I HAVE...

PERHAPS I SHOULD WARN YOU ABOUT THIS NEXT SCENE...

WHAT NEXT SCENE?

SPLASH!

8-11

THE PARTING OF THE RED SEA!

PEANUTS
featuring
"Good ol' Charlie Brown"
by Schulz

PLEASE DO NOT DISTURB!

"This is a case of murder," said the chief.

THERE HE IS WRITING AGAIN

8-25

DO YOU THINK HIS WRITING WILL EVER PUT BREAD ON THE TABLE?

IN HIS CASE, THE QUESTION IS, WILL HIS WRITING EVER PUT HORSEMEAT IN THE OL' DOG DISH?

HA HA HA HA!!

WHAT A SHOT...TWO HEADS WITH ONE TYPEWRITER!

PEANUTS
featuring "Good ol' Charlie Brown"
by Schulz

VETERAN FOR HIRE

SIGH

THE WAR IS OVER, AND THE WORLD WAR I FLYING ACE IS HOME...NERVOUS AND RESTLESS, HE SEARCHES FOR SOMETHING TO DO...

GIRLS AND ROOT BEER ARE NOT THE ANSWER!

BARNSTORMING! THE QUEST FOR ADVENTURE LEADS HIM TO BARNSTORMING!!

STATE FAIRS CLAMOR FOR HIS ACT!

STUNT FLYING! ADM 10

THE CROWDS SCREAM WITH TERROR AS HE PERFORMS INCREDIBLE AERIAL ACROBATICS...

OOO! AH! WOW! GEE!

AND NOW, HERE'S THE WORLD WAR I FLYING ACE PERFORMING HIS MOST DANGEROUS STUNT...

9-1

WING WALKING!

Schulz

PEANUTS featuring **"Good ol' Charlie Brown"** by Schulz

HOW MUCH? ANSWER! WHEN? ANSWER! WHO? ANSWER! ANSWER! ANSWER! ANSWER!

TRUE OR FALSE? ANSWER! FALSE OR TRUE? ANSWER! ANSWER! ANSWER! ANSWER!

PSST, SALLY... WAKE UP!! IT'S TIME FOR SCHOOL...

SCHOOL?!

I CAN'T GO TO SCHOOL! I'M NOT READY!!

I DON'T KNOW WHERE ITALY IS! I CAN'T SPELL "CAVALRY"!

WHO WAS THE FATHER OF RICHARD THE FIFTIETH? IS MY BOILED EGG READY? WHERE'S MY POCKET COMPUTER? WHERE'S MY LUNCH MONEY? I NEED ANSWERS!

HOW CAN I GO TO SCHOOL IF I DON'T KNOW ANY OF THE ANSWERS?

YOU DON'T HAVE TO KNOW THE ANSWERS... THAT'S WHY YOU GO TO SCHOOL...

SCHOOL IS FOR LEARNING

HA!

WHO WAS THE FATHER OF RICHARD THE FIFTIETH?

9-8

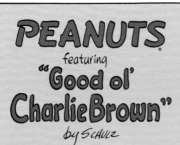

PEANUTS

featuring

"Good ol' Charlie Brown"

by Schulz

I KNOW THE ANSWER! I KNOW THE ANSWER!

THE ANSWER IS TWELVE!

IT ISN'T?

SIXTEEN? NINE? FORTY-TWO? ONE?

HOW WOULD IT BE IF I JUST SPELLED MISSISSIPPI?

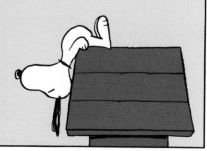

PEANUTS

featuring

"Good ol' Charlie Brown"

by Schulz

THIS IS THE GREAT NEW EXERCISE I'VE DEVELOPED...

YOU HAVE TO DO THIS FIFTY TIMES A DAY...

10-6

IT'S GOOD FOR YOUR NECK...

AND YOUR BACK...

AND YOUR

WUMP!

BUT IT RUINS YOUR BODY...

PEANUTS
featuring
"Good ol' Charlie Brown"
by SCHULZ

HERE'S THE WORLD FAMOUS BEAGLE SCOUT STARTING OFF ON A ROCK HUNTING EXPEDITION..

AH! HERE'S A NICE ONE...

OOOO! HERE'S A BEAUTY!

AH!

THIS IS YOUR ROCK COLLECTION? LET ME SEE...

BOY, WHAT A DUMB LOOKING ROCK COLLECTION! IT LOOKS LIKE YOU FOUND THEM ALL IN A DRIVEWAY!

NO ONE WOULD EVER BE INTERESTED IN A BUNCH OF ROCKS LIKE THAT..

NOT EVEN THEIR MOTHERS?

10-20

PEANUTS featuring "Good ol' Charlie Brown" by Schulz

HEE HEE HEE HEE HEE!

I BEG YOUR PARDON...

I DO NOT HAVE "RING AROUND THE COLLAR"!

12-1

PEANUTS
featuring "Good ol' Charlie Brown"
by Schulz

AND NOW IT IS MY PLEASURE TO INTRODUCE OUR SPEAKER.... MY STOMACH!

STOP COMPLAINING... IT'S NOT SUPPERTIME YET!

WOULD I LIE TO YOU?

WHEN IT'S SUPPERTIME, THE ROUND-HEADED KID WILL SHOW UP.... JUST BE PATIENT!

SEE? HERE HE IS NOW.... RIGHT ON TIME!

12-8

CHOMP CHOMP CHOMP!

NOW, AREN'T YOU ASHAMED OF YOURSELF?

I HATE A STOMACH THAT ALWAYS HAS TO HAVE THE LAST WORD!

PEANUTS

featuring

"Good ol' Charlie Brown"

by Schulz

TOMORROW IS BEETHOVEN'S BIRTHDAY... WHAT ARE YOU GOING TO BUY ME?

I'M NOT GOING TO BUY YOU ANYTHING!

YOU KNOW WHY? BECAUSE YOU DON'T CARE ANYTHING ABOUT BEETHOVEN! YOU NEVER HAVE!!

YOU DON'T CARE THAT HE SUFFERED! YOU DON'T CARE THAT HIS STOMACH HURT AND THAT HE COULDN'T HEAR!

YOU NEVER CARED THAT THE COUNTESS TURNED HIM DOWN, OR THAT THERESE MARRIED THE BARON INSTEAD OF HIM OR THAT LOBKOWITZ STOPPED HIS ANNUITY!!

12-15

IF THE COUNTESS HADN'T TURNED HIM DOWN, WOULD YOU BUY ME SOMETHING?

PEANUTS featuring "Good ol' Charlie Brown" by Schulz

The Gift

It was the holiday season.

She and her husband had decided to attend a performance of King Lear.

It was their first night out together in months.

During the second act one of the performers became ill.

The manager of the theater walked onto the stage, and asked, "Is there a doctor in the house?"

Her husband stood up, and shouted, "I have an honorary degree from Anderson College!"

It was at that moment when she decided not to get him anything for Christmas.

12-22

PEANUTS®

featuring "Good ol' Charlie Brown"

by Schulz

12-29

SNOOPY! WHY DON'T YOU COME INTO THE HOUSE, AND I'LL FEED YOU HERE? IT'S A LOT WARMER!

HOW NICE... AN INVITATION TO DINNER..

TAP TAP TAP

WHY DOES HE HAVE TO MAKE A BIG DEAL OUT OF EVERYTHING?

PEANUTS
featuring
"Good ol'
Charlie Brown"
by SCHULZ

1-26

RINGG

HELLO?

NO, I'M SORRY, SIR.. THERE'S NO ROOM SERVICE AFTER MIDNIGHT

RATS!

PEANUTS

featuring

"Good ol' Charlie Brown"

by Schulz

TRUTH

RATS!

IT'S TWO O'CLOCK IN THE MORNING, AND I'M WIDE AWAKE...

WHERE AM I GOING? WHAT AM I DOING? WHAT IS THE MEANING OF LIFE?

2-9

BAM BAM BAM BAM

Tm. Reg. U.S. Pat. Off. —All rights reserved
© 1975 by United Feature Syndicate, Inc.

I RECOGNIZE THAT KICK...THAT'S THE KICK OF SOMEONE WHO HAS AWAKENED IN THE MIDDLE OF THE NIGHT, AND WANTS TO KNOW THE MEANING OF LIFE...

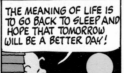

THE MEANING OF LIFE IS TO GO BACK TO SLEEP AND HOPE THAT TOMORROW WILL BE A BETTER DAY!

AND IF YOU'RE THINKING ABOUT EATING, FORGET IT!!

SLAM!!

WOULDN'T THAT UNPLUG YOUR HEATING PAD!!

SCHULZ

PEANUTS
featuring
"Good ol' Charlie Brown"
by SCHULZ

Allegretto

I NOTE THAT YOU DIDN'T SEND ME A VALENTINE THIS YEAR...

I HAVE THE FEELING THAT IT WAS NOT AN OVERSIGHT... I HAVE THE FEELING THAT IT WAS DELIBERATE!

HOWEVER....

..IF I AM WRONG, AND IF IT WAS MERELY AN OVERSIGHT OR IF THE VALENTINE THAT SPOKE SO ELOQUENTLY YOUR LOVE FOR ME WAS LOST IN THE MAIL, THEN I WANT TO EXPRESS MY APPRECIATION FOR THE THOUGHT!

2-16

IT WAS NOT AN OVERSIGHT, AND IT DID NOT GET LOST IN THE MAIL!

I SEE...WELL, YOU KNOW THE OLD SAYING...

WHAT OLD SAYING?

RATS!

PEANUTS
featuring
"Good ol' CharlieBrown"
by Schulz

CONNOISSEUR

RATS! I BURNED MY TOAST!

THROW IT OUT TO THE BIRDS...THEY DON'T KNOW THE DIFFERENCE...

3-2

Tm. Reg. U.S. Pat. Off. — All rights reserved
© 1975 by United Feature Syndicate, Inc.

SOME BIRDS DO!

Schulz

PEANUTS featuring "Good ol' CharlieBrown" by SCHULZ

I HATE PLAYING ON A WINDY DAY!!

PEANUTS featuring "Good ol' Charlie Brown" by Schulz

I DON'T BELIEVE IT!

HOW COME YOU'VE NEVER WORN THIS SHIRT THAT YOU GOT FOR CHRISTMAS?

IT HAS PINS IN IT!

CAN'T YOU TAKE THE PINS OUT?

IT ALSO HAS TAGS ON IT

COULDN'T YOU TAKE THE TAGS OFF?

THEY HAVE TO BE CUT OFF

COULDN'T YOU JUST CUT THEM OFF?

YOU HAVE TO HAVE A SCISSORS

WE MUST HAVE AT LEAST FIVE PAIRS OF SCISSORS AROUND THIS HOUSE...

3-16

I'D HAVE TO TRY TO FIND ONE OF THEM

IT'S ALSO PROBABLY NOT EVEN MY SIZE!

SCHULZ

PEANUTS featuring "Good ol' Charlie Brown" by Schulz

LUNCH TIME!

...LOTS OF ROOM RIGHT HERE, SWEETIE...

DO YOU WANT A BITE OF MY PEANUT BUTTER SANDWICH, LINUS?

NO, THANK YOU...I HAVE MY OWN

IT'S NICE HAVING LUNCH TOGETHER, ISN'T IT?

WE'RE NOT HAVING LUNCH TOGETHER... WE'RE JUST SITTING ON THE SAME BENCH

WHAT ARE THOSE BOYS PLAYING?

SOCCER...THE IDEA IS TO KICK THE BALL DOWN THE FIELD, AND...

3-23

ARE YOU HURT, LINUS? ARE YOU HURT?

GOOD GRIEF!

POOR SWEET BABY! ♥ SMAK ♥

?!

I'D LIKE TO SEE THE SCHOOL NURSE, PLEASE.. I GOT HIT BY A SOCCER BALL! NO, MY HEAD IS ALL RIGHT....

IT WAS THE KISS... I'VE GOT PEANUT BUTTER IN MY EYE!

PEANUTS featuring "Good ol' CharlieBrown" by Schulz

3-30

HOW CAN I SEE ANYTHING WITH YOUR STUPID HEAD IN THE WAY?

FORGET IT!

Schulz

This is a school project.. I'm drawing a map of the whole world...

I have to put in all the countries, and all the capitals, and all the mountains, and the rivers, and the trees, and the rocks and all the people!

Dot dot dot dot dot dot dot dot dot dot dot

This is the hardest part.. drawing in all their eyes...

I'm also putting in all the dogs and cats and bugs.. Do you realize how many bugs there are in the world?

There! It's finished! Now, I can go to bed knowing it's been a job well done...

She sure gets involved in some weird projects

Dot dot dot dot dot dot dot dot

4-13

I thought you were in bed... I thought you were finished...

I forgot horses and cows...

PEANUTS
featuring
"Good ol'
Charlie Brown"
by Schulz

SO IT'S RAINING A LITTLE! YOU CAN'T PLAY RIGHT FIELD WITH AN UMBRELLA OVER YOUR HEAD!

4-20

CHONK!

I CAN'T EVEN CRITICIZE GOOD..

PEANUTS
featuring
"Good ol' Charlie Brown"
by Schulz

MoM

Dear Mom,

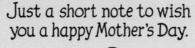

Just a short note to wish you a happy Mother's Day.

I miss you very much. I miss your hugs, your kisses and your apple pie.

I FIND IT HARD TO BELIEVE THAT YOUR MOTHER BAKED APPLE PIES...

HE'S RIGHT, OF COURSE..

5-11

MOM BELONGED TO A LITTLE THEATER GROUP, AND WAS NEVER HOME VERY MUCH!

PEANUTS

featuring

"Good ol' Charlie Brown"

by Schulz

WHAP!

5-18

POW

?

I THINK WHAT HE PROBABLY SAID WAS, "IF YOU THROW ONE MORE DUMB PITCH DOWN THE MIDDLE LIKE THAT, I'M GOING TO COME BACK HERE, AND BREAK YOUR ARM!"

EVERYONE IN THE STANDS IS AN EXPERT!

PEANUTS
featuring
"Good ol' Charlie Brown"
by SCHULZ

DON'T TREAD ON ME!

THE ONLY THING THAT KEEPS ME GOING IS TENURE..

BOY, WILL I BE GLAD WHEN SCHOOL IS OUT!

MY TEACHER HAS BEEN DRIVING ME CRAZY..

6-1

I THINK THE PRINCIPAL HATES ME..

ALL THE CUSTODIANS ARE CRABBY...

AND THE BUILDING ITSELF IS EITHER TOO HOT OR TOO COLD!

BONK!

NOW YOU'RE GETTING PERSONAL, KID!

PEANUTS
featuring
"Good ol' Charlie Brown"
by Schulz

MY SON, THE LOSER

OKAY, GANG, THIS IS IT!

ISN'T THAT YOUR DAD OVER THERE, CHARLIE BROWN?

UH HUH...HE SAID HE THOUGHT HE'D ENJOY SPENDING FATHER'S DAY WATCHING US PLAY BALL

WELL, YOU'D BETTER PITCH YOUR BEST..

MAKE HIM PROUD OF YOU, CHARLIE BROWN..

I'M GOING TO!

I'M DEDICATING THIS GAME TO YOU, DAD!

6-15

HAPPY FATHER'S DAY!!

POW!

WHEN HIS BIRTHDAY COMES, MAYBE I'LL JUST BUY HIM A NECKTIE...

PEANUTS
featuring
"Good ol'
Charlie Brown"
by SCHULZ

AND DON'T KICK IT OVER HERE AGAIN!

BLEAH TO YOU, TOO!

6-22

ALL RIGHT, I WARNED YOU GUYS!

GET THAT STUPID SOCCER BALL OUT OF HERE!!

THIS IS A BASEBALL FIELD, AND WE'RE GONNA KEEP IT THAT WAY!

THE REST OF YOU CAN TAKE YOUR STUPID GAMES SOMEWHERE ELSE! WHAT DO YOU THINK OF THAT?!

SCHULZ

PEANUTS featuring "*Good ol' Charlie Brown*" by Schulz

※ SIGH ※

DO YOU KNOW ANY GOOD RULES FOR LIVING, CHUCK?

KEEP THE BALL LOW..

DON'T LEAVE YOUR CRAYONS IN THE SUN, USE DENTAL FLOSS EVERY DAY, GIVE FOUR WEEKS NOTICE WHEN ORDERING A CHANGE OF ADDRESS AND DON'T SPILL THE SHOE POLISH!

ALWAYS KNOCK BEFORE ENTERING, DON'T LET THE ANTS GET IN THE SUGAR, NEVER VOLUNTEER TO BE PROGRAM CHAIRMAN, ALWAYS GET YOUR FIRST SERVE IN...

...AND FEED YOUR DOG WHENEVER HE'S HUNGRY

WILL THOSE RULES GIVE ME A BETTER LIFE, CHUCK?

A BETTER LIFE AND A FAT DOG!

6-29

RIVERSIDE, PHOENIX, EL PASO, PLAINVIEW, TULSA...

LINCOLN... MOLINE... TOLEDO... AND THEN BOYNE FALLS!

THAT'S TOLEDO, OHIO, DOWN THERE, SIR..

GOOD NAVIGATING, MARCIE! WE'RE IN THE TWENTY-EIGHTH ANNUAL "POWDER PUFF DERBY" AND WE'RE DOING GREAT!

ONE THING FOR SURE, SIR...WE'RE THE ONLY ONES IN THE RACE FLYING A SOPWITH CAMEL

HANG ON... WE'RE GOING IN FOR A LANDING...

HEY, MECHANIC, WE'VE JUST FLOWN ALL THE WAY FROM RIVERSIDE, CALIFORNIA... OUR ENGINE'S RUNNING A BIT ROUGH... CAN YOU HELP US?

* BOOT!

WHAT'S THE MATTER, MARCIE?

I DON'T KNOW, SIR... I JUST SORT OF FEEL TIRED AND DEPRESSED.. IT'S BEEN A LONG TRIP...

POOR SWEET BABY

♥ SMAK ♥

7-6

I FEEL BETTER NOW, SIR!

A GOOD MECHANIC UNDERSTANDS AIRPLANES AND WOMEN, MARCIE!

ON TO MICHIGAN

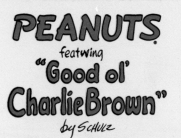

PEANUTS
featuring
"Good ol' Charlie Brown"
by SCHULZ

8-3

POOR WOODSTOCK..HE THOUGHT HE WAS AT A CARNIVAL!

PEANUTS
featuring
"Good ol' Charlie Brown"
by SCHULZ

WHEW

BOY, IT'S HOT TODAY!

IT'S ALMOST TOO HOT TO PLAY BASEBALL...I'LL BET IT'S TERRIBLE OUT THERE IN RIGHT FIELD, ISN'T IT?

DON'T GIVE IT A SECOND THOUGHT, MANAGER..WE'RE ALL IN THIS TOGETHER..WE ALL HAVE A JOB TO DO!

I'M AMAZED AT HER ATTITUDE

SHE'S USUALLY THE FIRST ONE TO COMPLAIN ABOUT ANYTHING

8-17

SCHULZ

PEANUTS
featuring
"Good ol' Charlie Brown"
by Schulz

IF IT'S JUST A MATTER OF LOOKING, I'VE LOOKED!

I'VE LOOKED FOR HAPPINESS AT HOME ♫ SIGH ♫

I'VE LOOKED ALL OVER THIS NEIGHBORHOOD FOR HAPPINESS... SOMEDAY, I'LL LOOK ALL OVER THIS COUNTRY FOR HAPPINESS...

AND, SOMEDAY, I'LL LOOK ALL AROUND THE WORLD FOR HAPPINESS, BUT I'LL PROBABLY NEVER FIND IT...

THEN, AFTER I'VE LOOKED ALL OVER THE WORLD, I'LL RETURN HOME

AND WHEN YOU RETURN HOME, YOU'LL FIND THE VERY HAPPINESS THAT WAS THERE ALL ALONG! IS THAT WHAT YOU'RE TRYING TO SAY?

NO, BUT MAYBE I'LL FIND THAT STUPID LITTLE PINK BRACELET I LOST YESTERDAY!

8-24

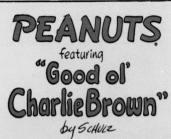

PEANUTS
featuring
"Good ol' CharlieBrown"
by Schulz

WHAT HAPPENED TO JUNE, JULY AND AUGUST?

※ SIGH ※

SCHOOL AGAIN! I CAN'T BELIEVE IT!

I'VE NEVER SEEN A SUMMER GO BY SO FAST IN ALL MY LIFE...

AND NOW SCHOOL AGAIN!

8-31

ANOTHER YEAR IN THIS CRUMMY OLD BUILDING!!

BONK!

DON'T CRITICIZE US SENIOR CITIZENS, KID!

SCHULZ

PEANUTS featuring "Good ol' CharlieBrown" by Schulz

PEANUTS

featuring

"Good ol' Charlie Brown"

by SCHULZ

FISHING?! I SUPPOSE IT'S NEVER OCCURRED TO YOU THAT FISHING IS A CRUEL SPORT?

WOULD YOU LIKE TO BE TRICKED INTO SWALLOWING A SHARP HOOK?

WOULD YOU LIKE TO BE JERKED AWAY FROM ALL YOUR FRIENDS AND TOSSED INTO A FRYING PAN?

YOU NEVER THINK ABOUT THINGS LIKE THAT, DO YOU?

10-12

SCHULZ

PEANUTS featuring "*Good ol' Charlie Brown*" by Schulz

10-26

PEANUTS

featuring

"Good ol' Charlie Brown"

by Schulz

Z

I'M AWAKE! THE ANSWER IS TWELVE!

GREAT BRITAIN! RICE AND BARLEY?

11-2

ABRAHAM LINCOLN! PIKE'S PEAK! THE OREGON TRAIL!

REALLY?

HOW EMBARRASSING

IT WAS TIME TO GO HOME!

PEANUTS featuring "Good ol' CharlieBrown" by Schulz

ONE, PLEASE...

WHAT'S THE NAME OF THIS MOVIE, LINUS?

IT'S CALLED "FEET"

IT'S ABOUT SOME FEET THAT TRAMPLE EVERYBODY, AND TAKE OVER THE WORLD

THAT SOUNDS GROSS...MAYBE I SHOULDN'T SEE IT...IF IT'S REALLY GROSS, I'LL FLIP OUT FOR SURE!

SUIT YOURSELF... ONE, PLEASE!

WHAT ARE YOU DOING HOME? I THOUGHT YOU WENT TO THE SHOW...

IT SOUNDED TOO SCARY... I DIDN'T GO IN...

THERE'S A GOOD ONE STARTING NEXT WEEK...IT'S CALLED "ELBOWS," AND IT'S ABOUT THESE GIANT ELBOWS WHO TAKE OVER THE UNIVERSE...

I THINK I'LL STAY IN BED NEXT WEEK

11-9

PEANUTS featuring "Good ol' CharlieBrown" by Schulz

Z

PSST! HEY, PRETTY GIRL! YOU WANT TO KNOW SOMETHING?

Z

I THINK YOU'RE KIND OF CUTE! YOU REALLY FASCINATE ME!

Z

I'VE ALWAYS BEEN FASCINATED BY YOU... I LOVE YOUR HAIR, AND YOUR EYES AND THE WAY YOU TALK...I GUESS I LOVE EVERYTHING ABOUT YOU,.....SWEET BABY!

Z

HA! I KNEW YOU WEREN'T ASLEEP!

RATS!

PEANUTS featuring "**Good ol' Charlie Brown**" by Schulz

HERE'S SOMETHING TO THINK ABOUT...

PICTURE THIS, IF YOU WILL...

YOU AND I ARE A NEWLY MARRIED COUPLE, SEE, AND YOU HAVE BEEN INVITED TO MOSCOW TO PARTICIPATE IN A PIANO COMPETITION...

YOU PERFORM BRILLIANTLY, BUT YOU LOSE! WHEN YOU ARE ASKED TO SAY A FEW WORDS TO THE PRESS, YOU ARE EXTREMELY GRACIOUS...

"I DON'T MIND LOSING," YOU SAY, "BECAUSE, AFTER ALL, I HAVE JUST MARRIED THE MOST WONDERFUL GIRL IN THE WORLD, AND SHE WILL ALWAYS BE MY PRIZE!"

12-21

HAHAHAHAHAHAHA

※ SIGH ※

PEANUTS

featuring

"Good ol' Charlie Brown"

by SCHULZ

DO NOT OPEN UNTIL EVER!

YOUR CHRISTMAS PRESENT?

12-28

TOO BIG? I CAN'T BELIEVE IT

SURE, I KNOW WHERE YOU LIVE.. I KNOW YOUR PLACE IS SMALL...

BUT I WAS SO PROUD OF WHAT I PICKED OUT BECAUSE I KNOW HOW LONELY YOU GET...

I ALSO KNOW YOU'RE NOT THE EASIEST PERSON IN THE WORLD TO BUY THINGS FOR...

BUT I GUESS I CAN SEE YOUR POINT

SCHULZ

PEANUTS featuring "Good ol' CharlieBrown" by Schulz

ONE, PLEASE

PAWPET SHOW Today

ARE YOU HERE AGAIN?

I ENJOY IT

SOME OF THE SHOWS ARE FUNNY... OTHERS ARE REALLY EXCITING...

2-29

THIS SCENE, OF COURSE, IS MY ALL-TIME FAVORITE...

THE CHARIOT RACE FROM "BEN HUR"

PEANUTS
featuring
"Good ol' CharlieBrown"
by SCHULZ

MOM
MÈRE
MUTTI
ANAQ
MAMÁ

YOU KNOW, YOU COULD SIT HERE FOR THE REST OF YOUR LIFE WAITING FOR YOUR MOM TO FLY BY...

SHE COULD BE IN ANCHORAGE, OR IN THE CARIBBEAN OR DULUTH FOR ALL YOU KNOW...

OR MAYBE SHE'S IN A BIRD CAGE SOMEWHERE AND...

OH, I DIDN'T MEAN IT! CUT OUT MY TONGUE!!

5-9

FORGET I SAID IT!! FORGET I SAID IT!!

THERE, THERE, LITTLE FRIEND... DON'T CRY...DON'T CRY...YOUR MOM'S NOT IN A BIRD CAGE...DON'T CRY...

SNIF

WE'LL JUST SIT HERE TOGETHER UNTIL YOUR MOM FLIES BY, AND THEN YOU CAN GIVE HER THE FLOWER...

WHO INVENTS THESE STUPID HOLIDAYS ANYWAY?!

SCHULZ

PEANUTS featuring **"Good ol' CharlieBrown"** by SCHULZ

MA'AM?

YES, I HAVE A QUESTION..

BEFORE THIS SEMESTER ENDS, MA'AM, MAY I ASK A QUESTION THAT HAS BOTHERED ME FOR YEARS?

5-16

OH, NO, MA'AM! NOTHING EMBARRASSING! HEAVEN FORBID, AS THEY SAY..

THIS IS SOMETHING THAT HAS DRIVEN STUDENTS MAD SINCE SCHOOLS BEGAN!

NO, IT'S NOT ABOUT SHAKESPEARE OR FRANCIS BACON... I KNOW ALL ABOUT HIM ALTHOUGH I ADMIT I KNOW NOTHING ABOUT HER

NO, THIS IS A PROBLEM THAT HAS BOTHERED EVERY KID WHO HAS EVER GONE TO SCHOOL...

WHY IS IT YOU NEVER CALL ON ME WHEN I KNOW THE ANSWER, BUT YOU ALWAYS CALL ON ME WHEN I DON'T?

SCHULZ

Other *Snoopy* books published by Ravette

Colour landscapes in this series

First Serve	£2.95
Be Prepared	£2.95
Stay Cool	£2.95
Shall We Dance?	£2.95
Come Fly With Me	£2.95
Let's Go	£2.95
Are Magic	£2.95

Black and white landscapes

It's a Dog's Life	£2.50
Roundup	£2.50
Freewheelin'	£2.50
Joe Cool	£2.50
Dogs Don't Eat Dessert	£2.50
You're on the Wrong Foot Again, Charlie Brown	£2.50

Snoopy Stars series

No 1	The Flying Ace	£1.95
No 2	The Matchmaker	£1.95
No 3	The Terror Of The Ice	£1.95
No 4	The Legal Beagle	£1.95
No 5	The Head Boy	£1.95
No 6	Man's Best Friend	£1.95
No 7	The Sportsman	£1.95
No 8	The Scourge of the Fairways	£1.95
No 9	The Branch Manager	£1.95
No 10	The World Famous Literary Ace	£1.95
No 11	The Great Pretender	£1.95
No 12	The Dog-Dish Gourmet	£1.95

All these books are available at your local bookshop or newsagent, or can be ordered direct from the publisher. Just tick the titles you require and fill in the form below. Prices and availability subject to change without notice.

Ravette Books Limited, 3 Glenside Estate, Star Road, Partridge Green, Horsham, West Sussex RH13 8RA

Please send a cheque or postal order and allow the following for postage and packing. UK: 45p for one book plus 30p for each additional book.

Name ....

Address ....

....